ADVENTURES OF ALVIN:

ADOPTION DAY

A L V. I N

STORY BY BRENDA DINGES
ART BY YOUNGJU KIM

ISBN: 978-0-578-36488-9

Written by Brenda Dinges
Edited by Eric Bell
Illustrated and designed by YoungJu Kim

TO CAROLYN,

OUR LIVES ARE FOREVER
BLESSED WITH ALVIN

Meet Alvin

When Alvin was born, he was 14" tall. He weighed 14 pounds and wore a small dog coat to help keep him warm during winter. He was very small but he had a big heart. He learned how to nurse his mother as soon as he could stand up after being born.

Alvin liked to play and frolic in the straw. He loved to run and kick up his feet! He thought he was as fast as all the big horses.

As Alvin grew, he became more curious about his surroundings. He would leave his mother's side and walk around his home.

He liked to greet the other animals.

He made friends and they would lie
in the sun after a hard day of playing.

He would stop by the pens of the other horses and talk about his day.

Alvin could be very naughty. He would pretend to not hear his mother call for him. He would also run around when it was time for bed instead of going into his pen.

Alvin loved his mother and she took very good care of him. One day, Alvin's mother told him that he could not stay with her forever. This made Alvin very sad. She explained to Alvin that once he gets older, he will go live with a new family.

Alvin's mother told him that foals are weaned at four months from their mothers. Once the foal is weaned, he will grow up to be an adult horse and he will have his own family to spend time with. Alvin's mother told him she will remember Alvin and will still love him very much.

She nuzzled him and made sure he knew
that he did nothing wrong.

ADOPTION DAY

Finally, Adoption Day has arrived!

Alvin is four months old and he is ready to be weaned off his mother.

Today Alvin's new family is picking him up and taking him to a new home.

Alvin is dressed up in his new halter and lead rope. Alvin is both scared and excited to meet his new family.

Alvin is so small he fits in a large dog crate to ride home to his new farm.

Alvin's new mom was adopted as a baby and understands what it is like to be a part of a new family. She also understands what it is like to not feel the same as other family members. She plans to make Alvin feel special and included.

Life on the New Farm

When he arrives at his new home, Alvin has a pen all to himself. He has fresh shavings that smell wonderful, and fresh water to drink. His new pen is warm inside and has a big area to play outside.

Alvin has a neighbor for a stall mate. His neighbor's name is Schmalls. He is a big sorrel gelding. He likes to stick out his tongue and nuzzle Alvin kindly. Alvin thinks Schmalls is nice.

When Alvin leaves his pen, Schmalls worries about Alvin and whinnies for him to return. When Alvin comes back to the pen, Schmalls is very happy and bucks and jumps with joy.

Alvin has two new sisters in his adopted family. Their names are Preslee and Allie. They were also adopted. Allie is a four-year-old Dalmatian. She was adopted at 8 weeks old. Allie licks Alvin on his face and likes to touch noses with him.

Preslee is a Tri-color Welsh Corgi. She is two years old and she was adopted at ten weeks. Preslee likes to run fast around Alvin's legs and Alvin likes to watch her. Sometimes Preslee likes to pretend she is grazing with Alvin and helps him eat grass. Both Preslee and Allie like to make Alvin feel special and included when they play.

Sometimes Alvin doesn't want to play. He tells his sisters this by pinning his ears back. He is careful not to bite or kick them because he knows this would hurt them and their feelings.

Alvin is learning to like the attention from his new family. He loves to be petted and have his ears scratched on his walks. He also likes to have his hair combed and brushed. He stands very still when he is bathed and feels handsome after he is clean.

Alvin's new mommy loves to give Alvin attention by giving him kisses on the nose.

Alvin has many new experiences at his new farm. He likes to explore his surroundings. Occasionally, Alvin will see a tractor or large piece of equipment that will scare him. Once he is able to explore and know that he will not be harmed, he will relax and return to grazing grass.

One way he learns about new things is to try and eat them. He does this to see if they will taste good.

Alvin's new mom likes to walk with sandals. He wonders if her toes are a new plant that might taste good. Alvin tries to eat them and his mommy tells him no! When Alvin's mother realizes he is sad, she gives him a big hug and a kiss on his nose so he knows she is not mad. This makes Alvin happy. He whinnies and kicks up his hooves.

Alvin loves his new home. He has made new friends and his family loves him and makes him feel loved and secure.

About Author and Alvin

Brenda lives in Western Kansas with her husband, Darren. They have three grown children and four grandchildren. Brenda and Darren work with one of their children-farming, ranching, and raising cattle and performance horses. Brenda is also a board-certified Family Nurse Practitioner.

Their animal family consists of two dogs, Allie and Preslee, and an enormous grumpy cat, Tuff. Alvin, the miniature horse, completed their family in July 2021. Brenda enjoys spending time with family, gardening, and writing children's books outside the farm and ranch work. Gunner, her grandson, has contributed to the development of the book. He is nine years old and is a cowboy.

Alvin, an adorable but sometimes naughty 28" tall miniature horse, is adopted by a family. He learns to adapt to his new home while making lifelong friends. Alvin must overcome change and rejection while learning to love his new family even if he is different from the other animals.

We hope you enjoyed our

Adventures of Alvin: Adoption Day.

ALV.IN

Coming soon
Adventures of Alvin: Making Friends
Adventures of Alvin: Going to a Barrel Race

Glossary

Bucks- A horse will plant its front two feet and kick up its back two legs. This can be considered misbehavior when a rider is on the back of the horse.

Dog Crate- Enclosed safe place for dogs to rest. These crates are made from plastic or metal.

Equipment-Supplies, tools, or large machinery used to perform specific job tasks.

Frolic- Cheerful, playful action.

Gelding- Adult male horse.

Grazing- Eating or snacking throughout the day on the grass.

Halter- A rope design that goes over the nose and behind the ears used to lead the animal.

Lead rope- A rope that attaches to the base of the halter to lead the horse.

Pens- A large enclosure that is safe for a horse to walk around within.

Pinning- A horse will lay its ears back when threatened, frightened, or angry. It is an aggressive signal from a horse to another animal.

Shavings- Safe, clean, and absorbent bedding for a horse placed inside a stall.

Sorrel- The color of a horse with a complete red-based color without any black. It is a bright reddish often seen with a lighter mane and tail (the light color is called flaxen).

Tractor- A large, powerful motorized vehicle used on a farm to load items or to plow the ground. The back tires are much larger than the front tires.

Weaned- Teaching an animal to eat other food sources than solely relying on their mother's milk.

Whinnies- A high-pitched gentle neigh sound that a horse makes.

CPSIA information can be obtained
at www.ICGtesting.com
Printed in the USA
LVHW071614050622
720532LV00005B/82